The Book of Frenzies

Pierian Springs Press

Gritty and zany as an early Bob Dylan song, Lindsey's poems are a delight, full of iguanas, crocodiles, and people often living on the edge, both during the pandemic and before. She captures the absurdity and bright light of her days and the purple velvet darkness of her nights, and ours.

Kevin Rabas
Kansas Poet Laureate, 2017-2019
Author, *More Than Words*

Lindsey Martin-Bowen's comic, often moving, Frenzies reverberate with the ghosts of Kenneth Patchen and Kenneth Koch as she invents a universe of whimsical revelations. These poems powerfully reject ordinary logic, and I find myself indulging in the poet's lofty imagination. These poems paint pictures, sing songs, tell jokes, and sometimes cry over spilled milk, as they walk their fanciful tightrope in a pink taffeta tutu, smiling, but only for serious effect. Negative capability wants its way with me, so I'm quite happy succumbing to these poems as they take me backyards into strange neighborhoods instead of a funeral or war-torn landscape. Lindsey herself so aptly sums it up when she says:

> "Or if poetry must be delirious and weird,
> or even a prophetic frenzy,
> then bury me in absurdia..."

Bob Haynes
Author, *The Grand Unified Theory*

The Book of Frenzies

Lindsey Martin-Bowen

Pierian Springs Press

First Edition
Library of Congress Control Number: 2022941167
ISBN 978-1-953136-10-7   Hardback
ISBN 978-1-953136-18-3   Paperback

Cover Design by Kurt Lovelace
Art by Romi49, licensed from Adobe, Inc
Body & Title set in **Monotype Sabon,** by Jan Tschichold
Flourishes set in Emigre Foundry **Dalliance,** by Frank Heine
Cover set in **Adobe Jenson,** by Robert Slimbach
Title pages set in 3 additional fonts:
Steamy, by Annastasia Samsonova, Jovanny Lemonad
Emigre Foundry **ZeitGuys,** by Bob Aufuldish, Eric Donelan
Emigre Foundry **Elliotts BlueEyeShadow,** by Elliott Peter Earls
Typefaces licensed through Adobe, Inc

PierianSpringsPress.Com
Sheridan, Wyoming

In memory of

Phil Miller, John Mark Eberhart, and Thomas Zvi Wilson,
who each appreciated, encouraged, and published
my early frenzies, which Tom deemed
akin "to Joãn Miro paintings."

A special thanks to Gary Lechliter, Silvia Kofler, Celeste Oster,
Carl Bettis, Nancy Eldridge, Pat Lawson, Penny Lewis-
Dunning, and j.d. tulloch, who published
frenzies in their literary magazines or as
sections of *Inside Virgil's Garage* and
Where Water Meets the Rock.

CONUNDRUMS

LAMPOONED LIT

DRIVING THE FLOWERS

CONUNDRUMS

"The poet's eye in
a fine frenzy rolling, doth
glance from heaven to
earth . . . gives to airy nothing
a local habitation . . ."

William Shakespeare
(*A Midsummer Night's Dream,* V.i.12)

Blue Submarine

Julio and Bonita were tired of Chiquita, who
kept tangoing on their lawn. Plus, she wouldn't
wear a mask, no matter how often they asked—
and she refused the Corona vaccine. So to escape
her and the COVID-19, they left the scene and
decided the best place to be was the bottom of
the sea—or at the least, in a comfy riverbed. They
texted Stan the Man, who owned Nancy the Iguana,
an expert skin diver who knew her way down under
the Grande Ronde waves. In five days, Julio and
Bonita trolled the Grande Ronde riverbed, where
Nancy introduced her friends, Tillie the Trout and
Sam the Salmon. The fishes laughed at anti-maskers.
"Down here," Tillie said, "all mammals must mask,
or they're done-for." About then, Ichabod the
Crawdad hobbled in, grinning. "Too many humans
aren't that smart. Just remember the Ark." To that,
Julio and Bonita said no more but decided
to explore the riverbed for the Crawdad's garden.
(They understood no octopi lived there.) Ichabod
gave them directions that only confused them. Still,
they enjoyed buoying around in the riverbed's
grounds but admitted they missed starry skies.

Under the Influence

It was like this—Mrs. Nimrod
looked down and spotted a crocodile
under the floorboards. "I'm waiting,"
the croc said, "for a vision." He dug
his claws into mud six feet deep
and started weeping. About this time,
ol' Lance McCann swaggered
around the corner with a .38 Mag.
A blue jay popped in and dropped
a big white one on his chin, while
the clouds, hanging low as toadstools,
slithered down the boulevard.
I chugged the last of the absinthe
and glared at the dead rabbit one
more time—his eye staring
with the blankness of a man who
knows night's closing in.

Swimming in Turkey Gravy

(with apologies to Russell Edson and Zbigniew Herbert)

To dig objects out of turkey gravy,
listen to the floating silence: There
a rubber duck, whiling away eternity,
backpeddles in water that freezes over.
The frozen lake dissolves into a man
eating mashed potatoes and gravy,
lifting forkfuls from the parquet floor.
Cross-legged on that floor, you sit
and envision strings of white-faced Indians
whirling in Wovoka's dance.
And these clambering ghosts
bring footsteps to your door.
Their knocking teaches you
the overturned pot and the dropped
goblet are gorgeous,
soaking with a duck that gives
the abrupt shriek of glass,
and the house explodes into fire
from burning potatoes and gravy.
Its language of flames
leaves you breathless
in a room where the bed, the chest
and the curtains remain silent,
inside here,
safe
from a crazy world.

Dripping Out

Amy needed to ditch her iguana.
"It can give us salmonella," she said,
crammed it into a pinstripe, and carted it to Club Med.
But the umpire said he wouldn't make it
through customs without a bigger slice of cheese,
unless a waltzing dead man traded his eyeballs
for a drink. In the meantime, Governor
Bellington scribbled a sestina on his umbrella
and turned his stanzas upside down. It didn't matter
much to Hester, as long as she didn't have to sell
her Pearl. But Arthur had a double-bypass
without gas or another anesthetic.
Just the same, he saw God
in a can of chili-beans,
which made him ready to tie one on.
Roger brought him cognac in a pan
without teflon, while he gnawed
on the last of the marble faun,
who got hooked on Levi jeans.

Hooked

Jasmine had a habit she couldn't quite kick,
so she torched it with a flamethrower she stole
from Madeline, who wore it as a talisman
on the train to New Jersey.
About this time, Abba grew weary
of their squabbling and shot them
with a wad of rain. Water rose
above the molding and sent their bed
floating downstream to the Gulf.
Meanwhile, Madeline awoke and packed
her elephant in a trunk. They bundled
up in an ark, lost now from Noah,
who'd quit eating ham, once he
found the burnt ends gave him
indigestion. He popped
an Alka-Seltzer and hallucinated
a plane wreck in Colorado,
where everyone drowned
but the cheese.

Economics

Jack Spratt could eat no fat
so Julio offered him a pickle.
But Jack didn't want that
and swallowed a Big Mac
from a microwave fiber. Supply-
demand, neither could understand,
and meanwhile, the orange juice
grew warmer as it waited
for a Little Mick. A Japanese
passion fruit flew in from Oahu,
rolled in chocolate, and hopped
a ship to the Apple. There,
stocks skyrocketed until
they bottomed
on the line and landed
with Jack and Julio
in an ice cream parlor.

Paid-Off

Davey and Moore scored
a lid they hid on their Harleys
and went searching
for Bob Marley in a New
Mexico re-hab. There they butted
into eternity's marble slab,
ever-lasting as chalk deposits
stacking up in Southwest
Kansas. They skidded on corn oil
and flew by pillars of smoke
that filled a courtroom
in Vegas, till they passed
a California tag offering
a hundred dollars to any
dad donating sperm—
HIV-positive or not.

Zip-Locked

"I need a ride," Mira said,
"to get me out of Houston."
The baglady said, "Hop in,"
and they tailgated a firetruck
to L.A. Two Pima Indians whizzed
by in a red Cadillac *en route*
to pick up a couple of keys.
Erica sat on their back bumper
and grinned, knowing the best
advice is none. So from
the passenger seat, Lamar
tossed her a doughnut.
Suddenly,
a policeman pulled up. "Pure
poetry's the opposite of reason,"
he said, then farted and popped
a Milk Dud. Meanwhile,
Bambi arrived
in a bodybag dumped
somewhere on the coast.

Edging

Juliet flashed a schoolbus,
lifted her Mickey Mouse and showed
her yabbos flopping wildly.
They took flight and lit upon a rooftop,
where a buzzard popped them.
When the cops arrived, a Van Gogh print
slapped their .45s with golden showers.
"We're beyond speaking," a Yorkie said.
"Just the same, I'll have some pudding."
I grabbed the mutt then remembered
in two hundred years of American
lit, no one ever farted. So I slid
out of the stall and headed
uptown, where a tabby in pajamas
hit me up for a twenty.
I had only one five and a dime,
so I climbed through the sink
and beat it home double-time,
banging my head on the newspaper
carpet. A doctor rushed in,
stinking of gin, and pumped iron
till the board fell on his head.
About this time, the neighbors
awoke, shot the Yorkie
and went back to bed.

To Rhumba the Waltz

Isabel got pregnant for the 45th time,
so another muchacha would do the haha
around the hacienda, where Bonita
gives dancing lessons. She rhumbas
in line with an iguana who left his hat
at the last station. Down the road,
a coyote chases an alligator so huge,
she moonlights as a parachute for a club
of mud-divers who just flew in from L.A.
After wallowing in rain, they turned back
to God, who sprayed them with another vision.
But the T.V. was turned off, so they
opened Dr. Spock and injected him
with cocaine. He arose from the grave
with a sunflower suit, polka-dotted
along the border. "It's okay to lose
your mind," he said, pinching
the choir boy in the ribs, "if you
have another to replace it."

Modeling

Listen—Lili balanced an Oxford on her head,
then slipped on an iguana, who'd dropped in
for breakfast. "Time's awastin'," the iguana said.
"And I need to clean my basement." So they
strolled down the boulevard, looking for a bus
with a back like a patched pair of jeans.
"How about a plate of eggs sunnyside?"
Lili said. But the iguana wanted eggs plated
upside down. Then the jeans loitered
on the street-corner for hours, trying
to pick up a can of peas. Meanwhile, the local
hermaphrodite let his purse bounce on a hip
while she walked down Troost, looking
for a place to sneeze. Bill the carpenter ran into
her or him, and they fell on a landing, which closed
last fall after too many thugs smashed walls,
grabbed gondolas, and ran past the bus
en route to New Orleans. But they split
up in Chicago, chased the drag queens
out of town, and headed back west,
where the sun's another egg-yolk
on a plate with red and purple greens.

Spinning

The first fly said to the second,
"Let's ditch this joint." So they caught a bus
heading East, then stowed away on a liner
crossing the Atlantic. Meanwhile, an iguana
hitchhiked from Covington, where he'd left
his psoriasis dancing. He gave them
a ticket to Oxford, and they jetted
to King James station. But the king was a shrimp
with an oversized crown, so at the Crossing,
he hired a barber to shape it.
They packed into a cab,
where Oliver twisted around
and picked their Gardens.
All was not lost: Jaggers
popped in with a pigeon
on his forehead. He bequeathed them
a scone so they climbed
through the funnel and landed at Kensington
Palace. Diana was gone, but left behind
a few mines to fuel them at the castle.
"That's enough," the iguana said,
"I need to borrow a scholar."

Re-Spinning

Tired of staring at ceilings,
the flies loitered
around Piccadilly Circus
and searched for an elephant
or at least, a hunk of cheese.
They flew to the twisted
treacles on the desk of the boss
in a London office
caught yawning.
There they held a wake
for their friend,
who died in an ink blot
bombing.

Regrets Redux

Julio and Isabel skipped school
and decided to plant a garden of regrets,
which the Brits call rue, that grew
in the Italian Alps. They took out a loan
from Jack, whom they'd regret paying back
when Julio slipped on a slice of cheese
from Monterey, after the festival jazzed it
up with jalapeños. So they phoned Lagrimas
the tall Iguana, a PT in a hacienda
not far from the Vatican border.
Lagrimas stretched Julio's back
till he was over the attack of muscular
anarchy. Then she gave in to drinking
Julio's gin but replaced it with a plastic
Bullwinkle statue. Like a spoiled brat,
Isabel grabbed that statue to join the gnome
in the garden. Before the massage was done,
two nuns arrived with Audrey the Willowy,
who'd spent the night with Richard
before Liz bonked her on the crown
with an empty bottle of Jim Beam.
Then everyone jumped into the pickup
and raced full-throttle to the cottage
on the edge of the foothills. There,
they finally grew a garden of rue,
and now, they sing the Blues
about regrets even still.

Waking Up in the Men's Dorm

Bonita had nowhere to sleep because she lost
her daddy's Jeep in the last revolution.
So she ran to Julio who had connections
in the local pet store, where an iguana
named Nancy worked for seeds and small
change. Nancy gave Julio a lead on a guy
who posted a sign for a roommate
at the center of town. Julio tossed these crumbs
to Bonita, who knew that again and again,
when she dug up dirt, she caught her fingers
in the cash register. So she shrugged and slid
into a stall, then out the door and ran into
Jimmy the Wrestler. Jimmy slapped cash
down her back and she used that as a deposit
on a new hacienda. But as it turned out,
the realtor doubted her clout with the priest
on the corner. So Bonita ducked out
and found a place with Ralph, a student
at the campus for runaway hounds.
This worked until classes resumed
and the dorm-master threw Bonita
out the window. She went back to Jimmy
who wrestled the realtor and bought
the hacienda on the hill. She lives there still
and bills the dorm-master for headache pills.

Chopped Liver

Julio unrolled his lariat and rode
with drovers while he looked for a cover
to his lap-top TV. And back at the ranch,
Bonita baked a batch of chopped liver
cookies for tonight's Scene. But she stopped
to give her iguana, Nancy, more dancing
lessons. So they cha-cha-cha-ed to the ha-ha's
and stepped into a tango. Meanwhile, Julio
lost his saddle when his horse Sancho lost
the poncho and reared. Along came Bonita
and Nancy, still dancing, which set Sancho
to prancing, so Julio had to chase the horse.
They formed a fine chorus line on the way
to the sun dance at the Gummy Bear breast-
implant factory. Fortunately, the sun
arrived with a hangover at five, smelling
of endive, before the dance was done. So
they had time to run back to the ranch
and grab the cookies, now for fun.

Fruit Salad

Julio brings
ripe pineapples.
I worry that a worm
will gnaw through the fruit's
thick husk and bite into sweet,
yellow meat before
Julio can eat it.
   He must know
a slice of pineapple
sweetens a piece of cholla,
even when someone sprinkles
lemon on it—or even
if a star falls from the sky
and chars it,
   the fruit
will stay sweet,
like the sparkle of a girl
dressed with bows
in her hair for her first
formal dance when she's
so young, she still wears
   burlap pants
to jump into a car
as if she were riding
a horse into a barn
after a rough day
of chasing cows
across the plains.

There's No Place like a Gnome

for Jason Denness

It was like this: Joey the Baboon couldn't find
his way home. At the street corner, he spotted
Oscar the Gnome, who traveled worldwide
posing for shots in Amelie's film. So
Joey asked Oscar for an autograph
and a pathway back to the school yard
where Julio hung out. Besides, Joey planned
to stick Julio for a ride. See, Julio toured
with Paul and Art, but took off Tuesdays
to drive Joey to basketball practice. And
today, Joey promised Oscar he'd nab him
free tickets to the Central Park Concert
if he'd lead him back to school. Being no fool,
Oscar took him up on the deal, tossed the baboon
into his Oscar Wiener-mobile, and they flew
to the school yard in a quick afternoon.
Even though Julio was about to fly
but stopped and gave Joey a ride. And
they got potted before the concert.
Just the same, all were pleased and agree,
there's no better place for a gnome.

Chihuahua City

Julio had enough of Great Danes.
So he decided to roll to Old Mexico's
desert and grab a pooch he knew
would appreciate life in the States, especially
after rains came and flooded the doggie
desert. Meanwhile, the Chihuahuas started
worrying about volcanoes and the woes
they'd bring. At any rate, Julio and Bonita
jumped into a jeep, circa '78, so the police
wouldn't likely swipe it. They flew over arroyos
and plains in the Chihuahua state, where they picked
up Charlie the Ape. He raised dogs and rented
out border collies, so he showed them a place
in the hills—the best spot for a Chihuahua haggle.
Looking like aliens with huge black eyes and
narrow cheeks, Chihuahuas sprang out of a creek.
Crawling from sand burrows, others whizzed through
skies, no surprise for Charlie and Julio.
Two tiny dogs shimmied across a log then dashed
to Julio and Bonita. They fed the pups cheese
and peanut butter creams, so the dogs leapt into
the jeep, and all four-wheeled home where
the Chihuahuas now roam Mexican tile floors
and tremble like *pinatas* in wind, never again
to be chased away from the States.

Vegetable Linguistics

1

Some sprout in earth—dirt,
rich mulch, where molecules
are born, split and fuse into more
cells, then sweet potatoes, carrots,
beets, and rutabagas—roots—
vegetable limbs sinking into blackness,
growing deep, building skin to protect
soft meat from animals and elements.

2

Some blossom—broccoli, cauliflower—
miniature coiffures of granny hair—
and shimmer with dew early during
June and July when morning
glories bloom and climb gates. These
veggies stay awake, feel wind against
their heads, wait for the perfect
hour before they lie in beds.

3

Others are towers—monuments
of phallic energy: Asparagus
stems stretch toward the sun,
artichokes spit spiky leaves
at the moon, and celery stalks
grow ridges for strength.
And can we name sugar cane
among these solid shoots?

4

And then come the fungi:
mushrooms bloom in wet
places, show button faces
in spaces where many
dare not step.
Amanita muscaria—
no, not yet.

More Vegetable Linguistics

1

José the Rutabaga was sick of
home-cooking so he opened
a bistro near *l'Arc de Triomphe*
where he last danced
under the moon in the grooves
between thick mulch, sweet
potatoes, and carrots. He asked Jack
the Beet to join in his feat,
where they could grow thick
skins to protect their soft meats
from beasts and other elements.

2

Simultaneously, Ms. Marie
Broccoli and her mama, Madame
Rene Cauliflower—with her granny
hair coiffure, opened a café inside
Le Louvre. Each morning, they
shimmer with dew during June
and July when morning glories
bloom and climb gates. They
awake early to bake all croissants
before eight, then feel wind against
their heads, while they await
the perfect hour to lie in bed.

3

But *la piece d'resistance*,
appeared in France when Francois
Asparagus opened a restaurant
beside the Eiffel Tower. It
exploded in phallic energy—
stems stretching toward sun,
and Henri Celery grew ridges
between his shoots that lasted
until Sister Elaine Artichoke
spit spiky leaves at the moon.

An Elephant-Lobster's Sea Garden

Dolby, an elephant-lobster wanted
to drop a few pounds to fit into his tux
for his high school's upcoming prom.
So wearing his silver crown, he dived
deep into the sea—down, down
to his watery garden where red and blue
coral surrounds lobster cousins who
shuttle through black sand and seaweed
waving like ribbons in wind. Dolby grabbed
Cousin Edgar and they hid there, then wiggled
antennae to lure minnows they'd slash
with claws. This diet was perfect, Dolby
knew, especially if a salmon or two swam
through, he'd raise his HDL. Meanwhile,
Edgar got lost while pursuing a jellyfish
who wished he'd never been born.

Dumpster Diving

It was one of those nights when the moon
was so high, it stumbled across the sky,
leaving streaks of light that caused Julio
to sneeze. Meanwhile, Ralph the crocodile
snored in the room next door. Now glassy-eyed,
Julio stared at the ceiling, then at skies outside,
popped over to Ralph's and booted
him to the floor. "Time to cruise," he
said and kicked Ralph again. Then
they hopped into Ralph's red coupe
and headed to Nancy's All-Night Diner,

where Audrey the Iguana hovered,
still in despair that she'd lost her
broad-brimmed hat. She slid to the wall,
to let Julio and Ralph into the stall,
and the three sped through a pot of Joe.
Then, they stared outside, to see a cloud
ride an eagle's shadow on the horizon
the last minutes before sunrise.

Dive-Bombing

Morgan the Fly needed a ride
to the rodeo in Pendleton, a
city in northeastern Oregon.
So he thumbed one with Evan the Buck,
who drove an oil rig west *en route*
to the Pacific Ocean. Meanwhile, Mack
the Jackalope wanted to smuggle
dope across dry Kansas plains and
avoid oil spills in alfalfa fields, on corn-silk
suits, or on a group of insane orangutans
who escaped from the St. Louis Zoo.
After Mack jumped into the cab
and stuffed his stash under the seat,
the orangutans scampered behind,
then hopped onto the tank, and got stuck
on metal hooks across the ceiling. They
started to screech, then threw banana debris
at a red Corvette whizzing by. Morgan
could take no more, so he flew out the door
and landed on the Corvette's floor,
where he still naps today.

Queen for a Day

Bonita picks up quarters on the porch
of an empty house, one the locals claim
is haunted. She disagrees, crawls
on her knees, and breaks into the foyer,
responding to Julio's dare to spend a week
there—on her own. Then some toadstools
appear and make her feel weird about taking
up Julio's taunt. Soon Ralph the Baboon
hears of Bonita's doom, plops into his SUV
and roars into the yard. His truck runs
so loud, a neighbor phones the Coast Guard,
which arrives on the scene with AR-15s
they hoarded from the last war.

Whirling Dervishes (of random thoughts)

"Some people never go crazy. What
boring lives they must lead."
Charles Bukowski

1

St. Francis d'Assisi rode a horse
draped in zebra skins,
a Medieval camouflage
that he thought made him
invisible to opposing warriors.
When I wear my long jumper—
a camouflage—designed to hide
soldiers in foliage or jungle,
I become invisible, too.

2

According to the Catechism,
Jesus was fully God and fully human.
He was especially a human
when he lugged that cross
on his striped back to Golgotha.
There, he left His earth suit
and morphed into pure Divinity—
not the candy, you silly,
but God almighty.

3

Like graffiti on a subway wall,
the ghost of Rappaccini's daughter
haunts me with gardenia smells
and confides her poison breath's
meant to heal. Her lilacs bloomed
today, and this year, they're huge
and smell like chocolate. And look:
The two toadstools down the street
still don't know what's happening.

Dervishes Whirling Again

> *"Some people never go crazy. What*
> *boring lives they must lead."*
> Charles Bukowski

1

I am Montauk. Rebecca Elizabeth,
an Indian Princess, born Ebonne,
Montauk Indian Tribe,
married Lt. Francis Bell, and
joined herself to the Brits here
in the states. After 12 generations
of begetting, those genes came to me.
But no father or mother,
grandfather or grandmother,
and so on up the tree
ever told me of this heritage.
So I became invisible, too.

2

According to some history books,
the Indigenous peoples kept
the air clean—no fire retardants to
cause mesothelioma, no asphalt roads,
no burning coal, no factories
spraying the atmosphere
with carbon monoxide.
And on and on.

3

Like graffiti on subway corridors,
the Pueblo painted bison and other
beasts on their cliff dwelling walls
in the Southwest. Was this the first
North American art apart from some
crashed Viking ships along Northeastern
Shores? Or were the Montauk
our first New York Artists
to display work outside of galleries?

Cashing a Check

It was like this: Isabel didn't know where to buy food
for Wanda her iguana, the one her sister gave her
for Christmas last year. So she headed to Pike's
Peak where she figured she'd hit a streak of good
luck because the sun shone mightily, and her Chevy
pickup bucked and leapt over sand dunes on the way.
Then she skidded into a mudslide where Harold
the Asp hid. This woke him, and he chased Wanda
the Iguana across the plain. Isabel downshifted
to third and pondered how absurd this race had become.
She shimmied to the right, wiggled past Harold
and the saline-blighted stream, far from mean Jimmy
Blowfish who bullies minnows. She found Joe's Bait
Shop and stopped to buy Wanda's lunch,
cashing a check she hoped would pay the tab.

Snowed-In

Julio opened the blinds to stare outside at clouds
smothering skies so much he and Bonita divined
a gigantic wedding veil had gone awry and choked
their tiny city till it became a ghost town bathed in
white. Snow battalions kept arriving like specters
of Russian soldiers ambushing villages in the Ukraine.
He wrapped himself in a parka and headed out with a
shovel to dig out his truck so he could drive again.
But the snow was so heavy and thick, he feared he'd be
sick after trying for an hour to remove it. Yet he also
feared they'd be locked-in with no food in their bins
so he phoned Willie the Giraffe, who often hit him up
for loans. Julio offered to drop the last one, if Willie could
fire his snow-blowing tractor and thereafter, blast through
the snow in Julio and Bonita's drive. Willie said okay, he'd
little to do that day, having cleared away all his snow.
Meanwhile, impatient Bonita had hopped outside when
Julio was bribing Willie. She'd slipped on any icy patch and
after that, couldn't stand up. So when Willie arrived, he and
Julio had to lift her and drive through snow to the ER where
they always go. While she stayed there in traction, Willie
and Julio found action at the local bar, where they
chugged mugs before they plowed their way home.

Snowed-In Again

It wasn't like last year, this winter.
Still, after melting in early February, the snow
logged in again before March. But this time,
Julio was ready. He'd learned from Willie
how to get the day rollin' with the snow-
blowin' tractor he'd driven all the way from LA,
much like ol' Dick Farnsworth did in *Straight Story*.
But his sweetie Bonita had other plans. Today, she
insisted he meet with Arthur, the chimpanzee
rebuilding their deck—connecting it to the bay
window he'd carved into a door. Then, whenever
spring arrives, she cried, they can hop outside after
dinner—catch afternoon breezes dancing on streams
of sunlight the tinted glass will filter with blue lights
to keep them cool. "How will I get there," Julio said,
then scoffed, "if I don't get this snow off?" Bonita
smiled and replied, "You silly man. Arthur will ride
his snow-plowing tractor here.

LAMPOONED LIT

*"A little learning is a dangerous thing.
Drink deep, or taste not the Pierian Spring;
There shallow draughts intoxicate the brain,
and drinking largely sobers us again."*

Alexander Pope
An Essay On Criticism (1711)

Anna Iguanina

Blame the trains—coupling, uncoupling—
clangs banged through Anna's brains—
till she grew insane and ran from Alexéi
(also Karénin) to Count Alexéi (also Vronsky)
and back again because she didn't want
to leave Sergéi (also Alexéich, also Seryózha,
also Kútik) behind. Her head pounded
through pages and pages, and all of these
Russians pondered and wandered
back and forth from St. Petersburg
to Moscow so Alexéi (also Karénin)
could beat his fist on the pow-wow
table. But no one was ready to revolt
yet, so they took another vote. And
only Levin (also Dmitrich, also Kóstya)
thought to till soil and plant wheat
after he left his sweaty feet at the office.
Then the trains railed back onto the scene,
leaving Anna in a lean and mean position.
And at the end, no yeast was left, so all
of them relied on Levin (also Dmitrich,
also Kóstya) to make the crops rise.

Paris Misérables

It was one of those nights when Cosette
caught her feet at every corner.
So she slipped into a fluffy pink robe
and wandered through *Le Louvre*
and down *l'avenue des Champs-Elysées*
in search of a polyester ferret—in case
she couldn't find Jean Valjean, who'd
promised her a wardrobe, much cash,
and a job gardening radishes. She
ran into a rodent who led her through
stringy paths in underground sewers
with rats and Left Bank detours—
all for another ball of cheese. At that,
Cosette hiccuped and sneezed,
causing her to tumble, flip back-
wards into *le Quartier Latin*,
where she break-danced
with Johnny the Fiend, while a
Le Moulin Rouge painter sweetly
romanced her by kissing her sleeve.
Still, she ran from the artist
romantically dancing to *la Tour Eiffel*
and floated aloft *l'Arc de Triomphe*
before she met a gnome, then
called it a day at a dark café where
she met two penguins named Ray
before hopping the last train home.

Oliver Twisted

O, what a morning it was—
when two salamanders took off
for London after Mr. Bumble
bloomed roses in Mrs. Squire's
heart. And Edward the Monk
with the map on his face disgraced
Nancy, whom Bill Sykes left
in a bloody heap on her floor.
Meanwhile, Fagan was hanged
in blood-stained silk from Selfridges's
bargain basement, while Ezekiel
cawed, "Nevermore." Then Rose blew
from the web onto Edward Monk's
head when he sailed to the India
holdings. Waving Ta-Ta, the Artful
Dodger strutted along, while Bill's
pit-bull snapped at his heels.

Audrey the Iguana Dances All Night

O, such a day it was—
with bright sun, no fog,
after Audrey the Iguana
danced on the staircase all
night long—at least, until the wee
hour before dawn, when two
salamanders delivered three
bottles of milk for morning tea.
Meanwhile, Henry the Crocodile
took off for London after Colonel
P sent roses to Audrey's room.
Just the same, Alfred the D
hit the scene really mean
and begged Audrey for cash.
So Henry returned and rescued
the waif, keeping her safe by
tossing Alfred enough pounds
to marry him to his paramour.
And Freddy the Goon crooned
to Audrey under the street lamps.
Nevertheless, although all was a mess,
Audrey sang her way to stardom,
no more had to face arrest
by the Bobby at Covington Gardens.

Vanities Squared

Becky Sharp had a vision, but it shimmered,
melted, then dripped from the sky like an overdone
apple pie we had to shuttle from the oven. *Why am I here?*
she wondered, *flying in circles and can't figure what I'm
to do. How can I get through this mess of a life so full of
strife with my opera-singing mother in rags, and my artist
father in prison. My purpose, it seems, escapes me, my
dreams elude my fingers as if they're wrens fluttering in
winds that make me shiver and feel like giving-in.*
But then, she decided, *Plato's ideal, mathematical
world might give her answers. Or at least, bring in some
cash that she could flash and use to build an empire.* So she
took two men two times apiece, then multiplied them by two
again. Already, this started her climbing stairs to prosperity.

Hot

Julio lost a pencil in the turnstile
at the airport. About then,
Dr. Dimmesdale bit into a watermelon
with seeds the size of New Jersey.
"There's nothing we can do,"
Scarlet said. "But there's always
tomorrow. Tomorrow *and*
tomorrow and tomorrow."
Natty Bumppo rushed in
to save them from sinning, but snagged
a toenail on his leather stocking.
Meanwhile, the humidity swooned,
moving them along like slugs hooked
on anesthesia. Then, the watermelon
waltzed with an ant, who'd just flown
in from some peonies doing time
in the pen. A nimbus dropped down,
swelled around Scarlet, and shoved
her on a train to Tara.
The doctor went home, groaning
for plaster that an alabaster
Hester slapped on his chest.

Fox Soup

O they hunted so long
that Jane and Liz, Mr. Darcy,
and of course, Mr. Bingley,
came along to that grassy space
behind the rose bushes in the front
lawn, where they'll corner the fox
who's been darting left and right,
fighting for his life in this wilderness
called England. But this remains
a pastoral spot, with poplars and oaks
across the lot, far away from London's
Baker Street, long before Sherlock
and John will meet and even longer
before anyone will conspire to erect
the V&A, where Albert and Victoria
rest today, not all that long
after they filled their bellies
with soup made from a fox.

Fox Soup II (at Downton Abbey)

O they hunted so long—
Lady Mary and Matthew,
trying to tie a tryst like those
in the days when Jane and Liz,
Mr. Darcy, and of course, Mr. Bingley
came along to that meadow an acre
away from the rose bushes edging
the lawn, where Richardson cornered
the fox who'd been darting left and right,
fighting for his life in the wilderness
called England. Even now, this remains
a pastoral spot, with poplars and oaks
across the lot, far away from London's
Baker Street, long after Sherlock
and John meet and even longer
before anyone conspired to erect
the V&A, where Albert and Victoria
still rest today—yet not all that long
after they filled their bellies
with soup made from a fox.

Red

Julio popped a bubble
that sent the boxcars in the wrong
direction. Farther down the line,
a pigeon straddled the tracks. "It
looks like rain," the bird said, "but
it's a good day for breakfast." Adam
looked down from a limb high
in the sky, a fig leaf caught
on an eyebrow, and frowned
because he couldn't fit into a red wheelbarrow.
But never mind the chickens—they hitched
a ride to stay with Aunt Naomi in Laramie,
where sunsets turn purple and scarlet.
"And don't forget the Apple,
  the Apple,
  the Apple,"
an Angel said. "Or Able. Better raise
a little Cain, too.
He can ride in the caboose."

Frazzled

Julio wanted mashed potatoes
so he drove to the kitchen in his beat-up,
red Ford pickup. Whizzing out of the lot,
he spun gravel, and two bald-headed cops
chased him to San Jose. There, they picked up
an armadillo for speeding and let Julio off
with a warning. So he tried not to get caught
in another newspaper scam when he slammed
down his brakes at a truck-stop. He picked up
Jose and they sped away to search for Audrey
the Iguana with huge green eyes. Audrey's land-
lady claimed that the Iguana moved away
to the West Coast where she lived
under a highway ramp near dessert dunes.
So Julio and Jose took another day to stop
for more gas, and then they headed West,
still looking for pudding they could spoon
on the way. When they arrived at 2:45 (AM),
they doubled-parked the truck at a B & B.
No one was home, so they left alone
and still search the West Coast highways
for Audrey the Iguana today.

My Flared Lady

Audrey, the thinnest Iguana, had always
wanted to portray Eliza Doolittle on a stage
in London, or perhaps Stratford one day.
But Rocky Raccoon, her manager, demanded,
"No stage for you. Yet what I can do, is stick
you in a rock opera—and you'll play opposite
that Rex the Red Squirrel who chased all those
girls at Chautauqua. As a matter of fact, they
chased him back, so you'd be a hit with all that
flack when you capture his cold heart with
your eyes flashing across the big screen."

The problem was Audrey couldn't sing. When
she tried, her voice came out gravelly, if not
in a scream. But Rocky wasn't so mean to
embarrass the Hollywood ingénue. So he hired
LaDonna, a ghost crooner to fill in the high
notes his iguana missed, allowing Audrey to
keep her honor. And clever Rocky knew, it was
quite true that slender Audrey looked flashier in
Victorian lace—especially with her big-eyed
face—than that Julie Bird—what's her face—
even if Julie's resonant voice had made the
stage her nesting place.

When the Cheetos Come Home from College

They've grown a bit rounder—
orange bellies drooping
over their sides—evidence
of the Freshman 15. Too many
restaurant scenes reveal
that tall tale is true. But
they'll eat celery all summer,
they say, to look good in plays
and TV commercials.

They tripped over Aristotle,
and Oedipus made them weep.
So they yak about changing majors
from theatre to movies—
especially those made for TV.
I tell them don't worry—
their talent lies in legends
and folklore, but they
don't listen to me.

I mention Rappaccini's
daughter—how her beauty
deceived the wisest ever.
They shrug then quiver.
This fall, they'll return
to where they learned
the lesson: *Applause*
sounds merely like rain
clouds bumping together.

Split Seconds

Julio tripped over Aristotle because the voices
inside his head led him to toddle to the Raven
and Readers World, where he sold his book
on macaroni and cheese. Meanwhile,
Ignacio loaded his holster with a paint gun
to have fun at this year's office picnic,
and he waited for Julio by the school garden.
Once Julio arrived, Ignacio stepped inside
the truck, sprayed Julio, who ducked,
and the paint hit a cop in the yard. Of course,
the cop burned red. Then he pulled out a guitar
and banged it on Ignacio's head. Ignacio
swooned then ran out but started to pout
while he headed toward the park
where the picnic already ran full-force.
The cop gave chase because he couldn't erase
the red spot on his forehead. Julio followed
them both and hoped he could share some toast
to end the ensuing dispute. Then Bonita appeared
with her cookies again and waved them at the cop
who stopped for a bite. So Ignacio escaped
but then met his fate against a paint gun larger
than Chicago. More paint is forecast tomorrow.

Roxanne*

It wasn't him, really.
Even if he was pretty,
I fell in love with the wind
wafting lily scents
across the terrace
and up the balcony
on a night when the moon's
an orange floating
on the Mediterranean—
or a pomegranate like one
Cyrano buys me in the market
on days when we talk of love.

I fell for his words—smooth
as dove wings. Cyrano's words
are sugar kisses, too. But his nose
keeps him untouchable. I can't see
behind his grotesque mask—
who can, really? Who sees
beyond the skin, beyond flesh
easily punctured by a knife,
a sword, or even a pin? It bleeds,
yet I still can't see within,
where muscles twitch
like insects about to take flight.

*The heroine in Edmond Rostand's 1897 play *Cyrano de Bergerac*.

Re-Tweaked

Juliet spent the night wondering what Romeo
might do if he arrived late in the local
saloon, and if he caught her talking with
Father Brown. Would that make him
down—surely he wouldn't think she'd
sleep with a priest, but she fidgeted
that night because sometime Romeo
was such a clown—a hothead about guys
who hit on her—even when she ignored
them—figured they just wanted someone
to whore around with.

She didn't think she'd be back—
she'd retired from the fashion
scene, all that modeling in
New York and the Paris Beats.

Then, that yearning came again
for ostrich feathers, satin,
and lace—all those frivolous
materials to accent her face.

Pride and Ridiculousness

You know the story: Elizabeth spat at
Mr. Darcy, who farted behind the iron-
ing curtain when no one was looking—
or standing nearby to sniff the air or catch
the sound of a motorboat, which, to Darcy's
regret, hadn't been invented yet. Nevertheless,
Darcy had snubbed Lizzy, which plunged
him into the mess. So afterwards, he had
to repent and re-access his pride and prejudice.
Meanwhile, Lizzy did her best to mop over her
pride at being a lit freak who avoided too
much gossip that'd leave her weak. Instead,
she preferred to read a novel and bat her eyes
so Darcy noted and emphasized she wasn't
like Bingley's sister Caroline, who wasn't very wise.
So to Darcy's dismay, their infatuation
began spinning along till he performed another
faux pas: He broke up Bingley's romance with
Jane, which not only caused Lizzy pain but made
her vow not to see him again. Still, Mr. D was no sleaze:
He financed the marriage for Lizzy's wayward sis,
Lydia, to Wickham, a rogue who'd misled her to elope
not that long after he'd brought woe to Darcy's sis,
Georgiana, a pianist and lovely sight to behold.
And all ends well as Jane's stories do—
with a double-wedding, decked in lace and flowers,
and a reception of legs of rams, thick rum pudding,
and salamander stew.

The Church of the Living Basketball

A roundballer dribbles
down an apse, while an eel rises
then vomits an ogre. Meanwhile,
three Mexicans line up for the 45th time
and weave communion wafers
into their ponchos. They dribble
and whine, then lay up baskets
around a rim of TV trays
that got lost in someone's hallway.
Meanwhile, Victor shoots a chalice of wine,
and shimmy-shake girls sing *Hallelujah*
in double-time while the clock
does the two-step. Then some cardinal
flies in, starts railing
about sin and sexual dis-
satisfaction. The referees flip
pancakes and call fowls
dirty names, like "chicken,
spud, and turdcake." Back at the ranch,
a palomino gallops in,
reeking of whiskey again,
and Roy and Dale give him
one more chance for redemption.

The Old Penguin and the Sea
(with apologies to Ernest Hemingway)

Why do old men wake so early? Patriago the Penguin
reflected. *Is it to have one longer day?*
He stared at the waves flowing toward him and watched
the sunlight glimmer with each fluid movement. Once again,
the sunlight burned. He sighed. *All my life the early sun
has hurt my eyes.* It was always that way, growing old,
perhaps. *Yet his eyes,* he knew, *were still good.* He shrugged
as the waves crept up the shore where he stood, albeit
crookedly, with that pain in his left leg. He'd had a good life,
fishing from dawn to sunset, staying mostly in the sun. Still,
so many times, he wished he had a bigger skiff and a huge,
covered dock to store it in. *But now was no time to think
of what he did not have. He must think of what
he could do with what there is.* Meanwhile, Francine the fish
swished by him again. He'd been stalking her for weeks,
unsure whether he should hook her and slap her
into a frying pan or just let her spawn upstream as if she
were a salmon, though she was not. She was a tuna,
a blue tuna. "O! you flirt," he shouted and heard his voice
echo through the surrounding hills. "You want to come
into my bed?" Then he realized, *If others heard me talking
outloud they would think that I am crazy.* He grinned,
shrugged, then reflected again, *But since I am not crazy,
I do not care.* Francine laughed. "Try to catch me,"
she retorted. She flipped her tail and leaped high
above the water, showing off all her power and beauty.
In fact, she appeared to glide in the air above the old Penguin
in the old, rotted skiff. Then she hit the waves
with a crash that sprayed the old penguin and his boat.

Just then the stern line came taut under his foot,
where he'd kept the line's loop, and he dropped his oars
and felt the weight of the enticing tuna's shivering tug
as he clasped the line and started to haul it in. Her shivering
increased as he pulled, and he saw Francine's blue tail
in the water and her golden sides before he swung her
over the rail and into the boat.

He smiled and said, *man is not made for defeat.*
His eyes glimmered.
A man can be destroyed but not defeated.

Cloud Power Rising

Adam Aardvark, the King of Hearts, needed some
cloud power within an hour. Yet he searched
another hour with no luck. So he stepped into a
truck-stop and devoured an ant who trickled across
the glass. Meanwhile, Vladmir the Steer had been
running in high gear 'cause he wanted to take over
the world without getting his sheets wet. So Adam
didn't know where to go for his Mojo until he ran
into Nurse Solly Gold, known for saving souls,
who boldly showed him how to fight insects and
other pests. She gave Adam a few hints and a hand-
ful of bats to help him conquer gnats who attack
with 3 AM egg-bombings. Once Adam conquered
those brats, he headed back to help the Cossacks
win their war. Along the way, he picked up
la Cage aux Folles but wasn't sure what to do
with it. Still, he remembered those days when
words could be read many ways and knowing
life's but a stage, he lugged *La Cage* to the
front. When he got there, he didn't despair for
all the soldiers shot each other and fell dead.
So the Aardvark was smart after all. He learned
still these days, that words can be read in punny
ways, and often, the world's just another onion.

DRIVING THE FLOWERS

*"The force that through the green fuse
drives the flower."*

Dylan Thomas

Death Might Be A Frenzy

When eternity's marble slab swings open,
the toads erode—curl in upon themselves
and tangle with iguanas
sashaying on the shore.

O what a night it is:
A wave drags pebbles into the sea
where the rocks build another condo—
another beach-front ball of cheese.

Meanwhile, cells starve for oxygen
and fly from uptight nuns in French caves.
And Audrey, the thinnest iguana
watches the souls of the toads rise.

From the Emerald City
to the Mountain of Quaff

(*or* This Must be Kansas)

Go out and get that long face lost, you say.
Bury me in Jerusalem, I reply.

I want to be one of the first to rise,
like yeast on a rock in the desert,

among iron stones, hills filled with brass,
in a land of olive oil and honey—

wrapped in silver and gold,
where water eats fire

and fire drowns water, and the angel
of the presence outlasts them both.

Or if poetry must be delirious and weird,
or even a prophetic frenzy,

then bury me in absurdia,
where the lemons bloom.

Jupiter Eating

On one of those lodge-pole
sort of days,
when the sun skis
across the plains
and a red cow
slides down a banister,
we rename the west.

We didn't start out this way
back in the wet days
when we rose from the swamp.
But when planets wander
in retrograde,
we climb that plateau
of pain to become stardust.

Doldrums

Tied to a bull that drug her
across the prairie, Bonita fell
under the spell of gardenia smells,
though sniffing them made her weary.
So she rolled a tumbleweed for cash
to find Julio on I-70 because he
gave her great deals on old Chevys.
Meanwhile, she fell in with Cedar
and Joan, two chimps from the Valley
who liked to get stoned and eat
mashed potatoes raw with no gravy.
Soon Bonita left the chimps
for Sloppy Joes and she bought
a Julio Chevy. Then, she zoomed
East, bought a spread colored red
in the Shenandoah Valley,
and won't go home again.

Doldrums II

O what a squall it is
that swirls us out to sea where Julio
sails in circles while he searches
for the biggest chunk of cheese.
Instead, he finds a Blue Moon—
maybe two—that he follows
over the edge of the world, at least
as far as the horizon leads,
glimmering with that twilight burst
before it's too bright to hide
in the ocean's shadows. And now,
smells of spring swell across Julio's
deck before he swabs it. Then he turns
astern and rams into Eddy the Worm
who's been sailing all day in a closet.
So we leap into a lifeboat and hope
it floats all the way to the office,
after the eighty days of rain
that pounded the frame
and pushed us to dock it.

Still Riding on the Storm

after the painting, "Forest,"
by Äsa Antalffy Eriksson

O *what a squall it is*—twirling
us out to sea, away from woods,
where Bonita steps through a threshold
and looks for the PJs she lost last week
when she swam under a windmill
until storm clouds roiled and shooed
her inside. There, she spotted a light
so bright, it dropped her into a garden
of regrets. And yet, she still steps
under that doorway every night
to find a way to play with the feather
that forever hovers in her brain. It watches
every movement she makes and reports
each one to the IRA.

Head Trip

Data left the Starship's trek and rescued
Julio from a wreck to help him drive a bus
of Decisions to the college Strategic
meetings. Audrey the Iguana blocked
them because her car broke a gasket
and she needed a ride to the Five & Dime
for a head of cheese to drop in her basket.
"Times awastin'," Poppa Decision said,
and he dreaded arriving late at the campus,
where a ruckus exploded in the lot
each morning at nine. So Audrey hopped in
without bringing her kin, her bookish Philippine
cousins who wore Levi jeans and paraded
around the breakfast nook. But before Audrey left,
the iguana kin stacked her car on blocks
and told her to look the other way. Instead,
Audrey gazed into the rear view mirror
where everything appears in reverse.
What's worse, Data hit the accelerator too hard,
and they took off, plopped on the campus lot,
where they disembarked in grasslands
and danced with dandelions forming
a ring around the asphalt canyon.

Happy Trails (1883 Re-visited)

Take, for instance, ol' Lance McCann, a mean-hearted
ranching man, who fell in love with a .38 mag. Now
Lance looked a bit like Sam Elliott, so he decided
to lead one more wagon train to the West Coast.
His niece, Bonita, had mailed him a flyer pitching
the Oregon Trail, so he took I-90 WEST, the best
route Confucius the Seer had spouted out.
He holstered his history and headed out on
his stallion Sequoia, through Idaho hills
offering few thrills under yellow skies
that seemed wise to his misunderstanding
this heavy undertaking. The flyer hadn't foretold
he was about to undergo another weary train
of woe until a young girl showed up. Looking
a bit like Bridget Bardot, she cantered up to
the wagon in tow. He knew then, he had
still more grass to mow, though he wasn't
sure what to do except to toss in a
salamander or two—and make a great
stew that would carry them all the way
through Wyoming.

Starry Night above Black Water

It was one of those days when Julio
felt lower than a grave till he watched a one-
legged man limp with a cane across the parking
lot. Though Julio wanted to write him love letters,
he thought it'd be better to write poems about
erotic crocs, enigmatic iguanas, and girls in pink hats
that look like duck buttocks. To bring Julio out of his
funk, Bonita appeared with her endearing elephant
earrings she'd inserted for his amusement. The two
escaped in a jeep Bonita picked up on the cheap,
and they circled Green Lake in the Rockies for hours.
Skies were so bright there—with Orion shooting his
arrows and spears, they quit caring about the Congress
that sent them grave-digging that morn.

Fizzing-Out under a Golden Moon

It happened like this: The moon hung low in the sky,
looking like a giant eyeball caught between black lines
that twittered and danced like butterflies gone awry,
when Bonita cried after she saw what she'd hoped
was a half-full canister of flour now harboring mere
ghosts of white powder. So she flew to each grocery in
the tiny city, but returned home without any. After
slamming the front door, she threw up her hands
and roared, "I can't take this Pandemic anymore.
Now, I can't bake your birthday cake. We're out of
flour and so are the stores."

   The situation was grim, and Julio knew it
must end. So he whisked out the door, shoved
his gearshift to four as he sped down to Allie Gator's.
Allie was a wise Cat, who knew that Pendleton would
have flour galore at a number of stores. So they hopped
into his Subaru, Allie pressing his clutch to the floor,
'cause they'd need to arrive before Wal-Mart closed its doors.
He hit 95 within 10, yet didn't notice the flashing red lights
behind him. A siren whined, and soon Jake Big-Bird pulled
alongside. "Pull over!" he screamed, sounding mean,
because he didn't know how else to stop the men.

   "Hey, Jake! Give us a break!" Julio yelled. "Bonita's
out of flour. And it's my birthday just four more hours."
Jake scowled a second, then relented. "All right—but here's
the deal: I'll give you an escort, but you can't report it—and
you'll owe me one big, fat meal." So off they flew, police
car in tow with the Subaru, after Julio wrote Jake an IOU,
which he still has to pay to this day.

Silent Canopy

In memory of James Tate
(December 8, 1943 — July 8, 2015)

Under Caribbean skies, a penguin leads his brood
through tall grasses where cockatiels fly and alight
on branches. The arctic birds dart around snakes

and perform poisonous dances and gymnastics
in jagged steps, toes turning inward, whirling
away from vipers until everyone keels over in a sweat.

Most of the penguins don't dig this hot aquatic scene
with thick palms instead of evergreens under skies
flat as blue paint inside a Victorian canopy for a royal

wedding. And smells of poi and hot spices don't do
their bills justice. They prefer salmon from icy seas,
where they swim and dive deep—far from a glowering sun.

Tonight, they'll try not to stink when they soak their feet
in Epson-salt water, sip a pear drink, and seek out a sailor
to help them find a ball of cheese, the perfect ball of Cheese.

It's Never like the Movies

for my father

this dying: no background chords
rising to a crescendo,
no *adagio* of strings.
You watch these ants, instead,
trickle across peonies.
They disappear. And you
can't keep your grip
on that granite wall of reason
but slip downstream
into some wild current
till you run aground.
There, you search
for the deserted place, a Holy Land,
where Elijah met God.
Even if you're hiking
the Appalachian Trail, up
Standing Indian Mountain,
you watch vultures circle
in and out of clouds festering
into some murky, yellow soup.
And when lightning hits,
Father Davis says Hail Marys—
and there, on the horizon,
you see Wovoka whirl
in his dance of ghosts.

It Isn't like the Opera, Either

(*Companion Piece to* "It's Never Like the Movies")

for Ruth Bader Ginsburg
(March 15, 1933 — September 18, 2020)

this slow ebbing away—
not like Tosca leaping
off a parapet
to her death—

or a corundum-colored
clash of swords in
a duel ending
a wild conundrum.

Instead, you
step into a woods
after the sun slips
behind cliffs,

and pine needles
hover, turning
paths dark.
You tiptoe

across thin grass
around stones
and coves where
toadstools bark

in voices creating
choruses Handel
might have woven
into a new *Messiah*.

Criss-Crossing the Mojave

Listen once again: Julio and Bonita decided to
ride west on his Triumph 650. Although antique,
it was still nifty for getting them out of Kansas.
So they zoomed through Colorado, then
swung down through New Mexico on to
California's Mojave where hot winds hit
their faces so hard, they stopped, and poked
around until they found a calyx a million years
old. "The air here tastes dusty," Julio quipped,
"and smells like fish dried on a shore"

"Maybe the smell's from this graveyard
of shells," Bonita said, picked up one and
held it to her nose. "The Pacific left behind
this graveyard of shells and rock when it
ebbed back to the sea. And look! There's
a diamond—and a garnet—just for me."

Acknowledgments

I would like to thank the following publications for which these poems have appeared or are forthcoming:

This collection of Frenzies comprises most of those appearing in two other collections—and many that will be in *CASHING CHECKS with Jim Morrison* (redbat books April 2023).

"Blue Submarine," in *Thorny Locust* (June 2022).

"There's No Place like a Gnome" appeared on Jason Denness's *Gnome* webpage (May 2019).

Then, these poems appeared in my *Inside Virgil's Garage* (Chatter House Press 2013):

"Under the Influence" (originally in *The Kansas City Star*, November 23, 2003), "Paid-off," "Zip-locked" (originally in *I-70 Review*, 2004), "Red" and "Swimming in Turkey Gravy" (both originally in *Thorny Locust*, S/F 2008); "Swimming in Turkey Gravy," also this summer in *Contemporary Surrealist and Magical Realist Poetry Anthology* (Lamar University Press) compiled and edited by Dr. Jonas Zdanys, *Professor Emeritis*, Sacred Heart University; "Edging" (originally in *Thorny Locust* S/S 2012), "Hooked" (originally in *The Same*, November 2008),"Modelling," "Hot," "Spinning," "Re-Spinning," "Death May be a Frenzy," "It's never like the movies" (originally *in I-70 Review* (2004) also in *Standing on the Edge of the World* (Woodley Press/Washburn University 2008), and *The Writers Place Yearbook 2021* (Kansas City, Missouri).

The collection, *Where Water Meets the Rock* (39 WEST PRESS 2017) included these frenzies: "Economics" (originally in *Thorny Locust* Issue 2/2017), "Roxanne," "Backyard Burial" (originally in *New Letters*, Vol.75/4 2009) and *Inside Virgil's Garage* (Chatter House 2013), "Oliver Twisted" (originally in *Tittynope Zine*, Issue 2, 2017), "Regrets Redux," "Anna Iguanina," "Frazzled" (originally in *Tittynope Zine*, Issue 1, 2016), "Waking up in the Men's Dorm," "When the Cheetos Came Home from College," "Fruit Salad," "Doldrums," "Doldrums II," "Still Riding on the Storm," "Chopped Liver," "Fox Soup" (originally in *The Same*, 2017), "Silent Canopy" (originally in *Phantom Drift*, 2017), "Whirling Dervishes (of random thoughts)" (originally in *Tittynope Zine*, Issue 2, 2017), "Vegetable Linguistics," Honorable Mention, Non-Rhyming Poetry, 85th Annual *Writers Digest* Contest (2016), originally in *I-70 Review* (2017).

The following will appear in *CASHING CHECKS with Jim Morrison* (redbat books 2023): "Chihuahua City," "Audrey the Iguana," "More Vegetable Linguistics," "An Elephant-Lobster's Sea Garden," "Fox Soup II," "Dumpster-Diving," "Dive-Bombing," "Queen for a Day," Dervishes Whirling Again," "Starry Night above Black Water," "Cashing a Check" (originally in *Thorny Locust*, Vol. 24.1, 2018).

Lindsey Martin-Bowen

Lindsey Martin-Bowen

Lindsey Martin-Bowen's fourth poetry collection, *Where Water Meets the Rock* was nominated for a Pulitzer Prize, her third, *CROSSING KANSAS with Jim Morrison* (in chapbook form) was a semi-finalist in the QuillsEdge Press 2015-2016 Chapbook Contest. In 2017, it won the Kansas Writers Association award, "Looks Like a Million."

In 2016, Writer's Digest gave her *"Vegetable Linguistics"* an Honorable Mention in its 85th Annual Contest (Non-rhyming Poetry Category). Her *Inside Virgil's Garage* (Chatter House Press 2013) was a runner-up in the 2015 Nelson Poetry Book Award, and a poem from that collection was nominated for a Pushcart Prize. McClatchy Newspapers named her *Standing on the Edge of the World* (Woodley Press/Washburn University) one of the Ten Top Poetry Books of 2008. It was nominated for a Pen Award. Her poems have run in *New Letters, I-70 Review, Thorny Locust, Tittynope Zine, Coal City Review, Amethyst Arsenic, Silver Birch Press, Flint Hills Review, Bare Root Review, The Same, Phantom Drift, Porter Gulch Review, Rockhurst Review*, 21 anthologies, and other literary magazines. She taught at the University of Missouri-Kansas City 18 years and often concurrently at MCC-Longview 25 years, and now she teaches writing, Criminal Law, Criminal Procedure, and American Court Systems and Practices (online) for Blue Mountain Community College in Pendleton, Oregon. She holds an MA from the University of Missouri and a *Juris Doctor* degree from the UMKC Law School.

In a previous life, Lindsey was a full-time newspaper reporter for *The Louisville Times* (Louisville, Colorado) and for *The SUN* Newspapers (Johnson County, Kansas), an associate editor for *Modern Jeweler Magazine* and the editor for *The National Paralegal Reporter*.

also by Lindsey Martin-Bowen

Poetry

Where Water Meets the Rock
(39 West Press 2017)

CROSSING KANSAS with Jim Morrison
(Paladin Contemporaries 2016)

Inside Virgil's Garage
(Chatter House Press 2013)

Standing on the Edge of the World
(Woodley Press/Washburn University 2008)

Second Touch
(Chapbook 1990)

Fiction

Rapture Redux: A Comedy
(Paladin Contemporaries 2014)

Hamburger Haven
(Paladin Contemporaries 2009)

Cicada Grove
(Paladin Contemporaries 1992)

Made in the USA
Monee, IL
18 October 2022

16129087R00062